GEORG PHILIPP TELEMANN

FANTASIAS (First Dozen)

Edited by Richard Jones

THE ASSOCIATED BOARD OF
THE ROYAL SCHOOLS OF MUSIC

INTRODUCTION

The present edition contains the first dozen of Telemann's three dozen Fantasias which were originally published by the composer under the title: FANTAISIES/POUR/LE CLAVESSIN;/3 Douzaines./PAR/TELEMANN. [Hamburg, 1732/3]. Like Bach a few years later in the Second Part of the *Clavierübung* (the Italian Concerto and French Overture), Telemann sets out deliberately to juxtapose the French and Italian styles: of his Fantasias, the first and third dozen have Italian titles and tempo markings; the second dozen French.

Each of the first twelve Fantasias consists of three movements, of which the middle one is a brief slow movement in a related key, and the third a repeat of the first. Telemann further intends that this ABA movement-structure should be reflected in an ABA arrangement of pieces: strictly speaking, they are to be performed in groups as follows: 121/343/565/787/9 10 9/11 12 11. However, since this method of performance involves a lot of repetition – one of the movements in each group has to be played four times over – most musicians today will probably prefer to play the Fantasias singly.

This practical edition is based on the exemplar of the original edition in the Paul Hirsch Collection (Hirsch III. 538) which is now housed in the British Library. The editorial aim has been to present a text that allows as stylish a rendering as possible, allowing for the fact that the majority of players will be pianists rather than harpsichordists. Inner parts and additional harmony notes, which would have been improvised by the player in an 18th century performance, have been inserted in small print, particularly in the slow movements. And indications are given, again in small print, of cases in which harmony notes would have been sustained beyond their notated value (e.g. Fantasia no.1, R.H., bb.1-2).

Telemann's staccato wedges have been reproduced as dots and his cruciform shakes (+) as ⇜, ⇝, or tr according to context. All tempo markings are authentic, but any other expression marks (e.g. *rit.*, *cantabile*) and all dynamics, fingering and metronome marks are editorial. The phrasing is editorial unless otherwise stated. Finally, editorial ornaments and arpeggio signs are given in square brackets.

RICHARD JONES
Oxford, 1983

Fantasia no. 1 in D

TELEMANN

Allegro [♪ = c. 132]

AB 1823

Adagio [♪ = c. 72]

Allegro D.C.

Fantasia no. 2 in D minor

Presto D.C.

Fantasia no. 3 in E

Editorial Note: The slurs to the appoggiaturas in bb. 14, 16, 49 - 51, 56 and 58 are Telemann's. He also has a staccato wedge at the first R.H. note of bar 28.

Largo [♩ = c. 60]

Editorial Note: The slurs in bb. 5-6, 9-10 and 17-18 are Telemann's.
The repeats could be varied at bb. 1 and 11 as follows:

and

Vivace D.C.

Fantasia no. 4 in E minor

Allegro D.C.

Fantasia no. 5 in F

Editorial Note: In the original edition the fifth bass note in b. 40 is F – presumably an error (cf. bb. 41 and 18-19).

Largo [♩ = c.40]

Vivace D.C.

Fantasia no. 6 in F minor

Tempo di Minuetto [♪ = c.132]

Editorial Note: The slurs in the R.H. in bb. **1, 3, 10-12, 17, 53, 55, 58-60** and **64-68** are Telemann's.

Largo [♩ = c. 76]

Tempo di Minuetto D.C.

Fantasia no. 7 in G

Largo [♪ = c. 112]

cantabile

Editorial Note: The staccatos in bb. 6 & 13 and the treble slur in b. 8 are Telemann's.

Presto D.C.

AB 1823

Fantasia no. 8 in G minor

Editorial Note: The bass note at the 2nd beat of b. 23 is e¹ in the original edition; it has been corrected to c¹ in pencil in the British Library copy.

Cantabile [♩ = c.60]

Vivace D.C.

Note: The editorial ornaments in bb. 6-10 and 17-22 provide a means of varying the repeats.

Fantasia no. 9 in A

Editorial Note: The staccatos in bb. 1-2, 20-21 and 31-32 are Telemann's.

Allegro D.C.

Fantasia no. 10 in A minor

Allegro [♩ = c. 120]

Editorial Note: The 4th bass note of b. 60 is e in the original edition, but cf. bb. 17-18, 46-47 and 58.

— so ? its the last 5 its kind
perhaps he meant to round
it off ?

Largo [♩ = c.69]

p sempre legato

simile

mp

simile

simile

rit.

Allegro D.C.

Editorial Note: b. 3, 1st quaver, c¹ natural: crotchet in original edition.

Fantasia no. 11 in B flat

Editorial Note: The staccatos in b. 27, R.H., are Telemann's. In the original edition the 3rd R.H. note in b. 47 is a¹, but cf. the two preceding sequential steps.

Largo [♩ = c.88]

Editorial Note: The staccatos in bb. 4 and 12 (except the last in b. 4) are Telemann's.

Allegro D.C.

Fantasia no.12 in E flat

Largo [♩ = c. 63]

Vivace D.C.

AB 1823